THE NAUGHTY WORLD OF ALBERT HERBERT HAWKINS

FRANK DICKENS

GRUB STREET LONDON

First published in Great Britain in 1990 by
Grub Street, The Basement, 10 Chivalry Rd
London SW11 1HT

British Library Cataloguing in Publication Data
Dickens, Frank 1931-
The naughty world of Albert Herbert Hawkins.
I. Title
823.914 [J]
ISBN 0-948817-39-9

Printed and bound in Great Britain by
Richard Clay Ltd

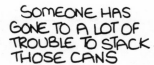

SOMEONE HAS GONE TO A LOT OF TROUBLE TO STACK THOSE CANS

FINGERS STOP TWITCHING.... EYES STOP SPARKLING....

PLEASE CAN YOU HAND ME ONE OF THOSE?

I CAN'T REACH THE TOP SHELF... WOULD YOU MIND?

LET ME GET THAT FOR YOU, SONNY

THAT'S VERY KIND OF YOU.....

LET THE LITTLE BOY GO FIRST....

FIFTY TWO DOLLARS PLEASE.

THAT'S FUNNY — I SEEM TO HAVE COME OUT WITHOUT ANY MONEY......

EVERYONE KEEPS TELLING ME HOW SMART I LOOK TODAY....

IT'S FUNNY, REALLY... I'M WEARING THE SAME CLOTHES AS I WORE YESTERDAY... I HAVEN'T CHANGED A THING....

I'VE JUST CLEANED MY BADGES.....

442

THE WORLD FAMOUS BIG GAME HUNTER SEES ANIMAL TRACKS...

MOOSE? CROCODILE? ELEPHANT? GIRAFFE? SNAKE? RHINO? ZEBRA?

NEXT DOOR'S CAT....

334

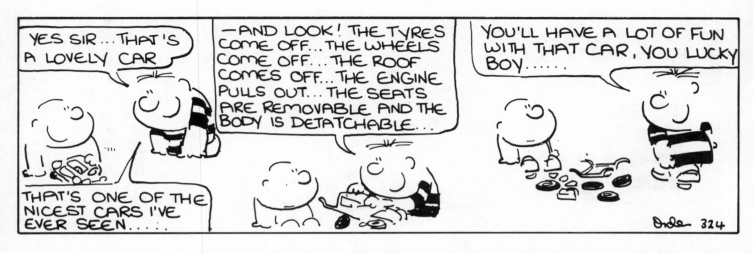

179

526

MY HOROSCOPE TELLS ME TO BE VERY CAREFUL. THERE IS TROUBLE AHEAD.

LIBRARY

I'D LIKE TO JOIN THE LIBRARY, PLEASE....

ALBERT HERBERT HAWKINS? THAT NAME RINGS A BELL... I HOPE YOU'RE NOT THAT NAUGHTY BOY IN MY SON'S CLASS AT SCHOOL...

LIBRARIAN

SILENCE

NO, THAT'S MY BROTHER. HE DOESN'T WEAR SPECTACLES.

OFF YOU GO THEN, DEAR — CHOOSE A NICE BOOK

CAN I STAY HERE ALL DAY?

OF COURSE.. AS LONG AS YOU'RE QUIET

THANK YOU.

NOW THEN.... WHERE TO START...?

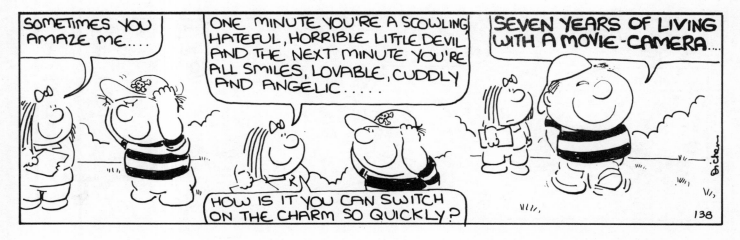

507

474

OOPS! BUTTERFINGERS!

KEEP OFF THE GRASS

OOPS! BUTTERFEET!

THUD!

KEEP OFF THE GRASS

HEY, COME OFF THERE! CAN'T YOU READ?

KEEP OFF THE GRASS

I DON'T CARE ABOUT YOUR BALL... KEEP OFF THE GRASS!

WILLIE — COME WITH ME — I WANT TO SHOW YOU SOMETHING......

WAR AND PEACE L. TOLSTOI

THAT'S MY VERY BEST BALL OVER THERE......

DON'T YOU DARE PLAY WITH IT BECAUSE IT'S NOT YOURS AND IT'S ONLY FOR BIG BOYS TO PLAY WITH......

KEEP OFF GRASS

I'M GOING TO TAKE A SHORT WALK........

246

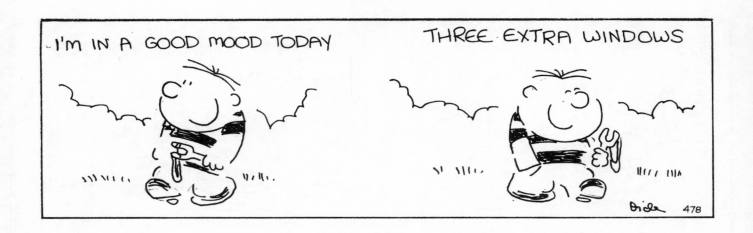

TO BE OR NOT TO BE
NAUGHTY... THAT IS THE
QUESTION